No Faith Required

W0007219

No Faith Required

Matthew Manning

Eikstein Publications

First published 1995

ISBN 82-90601-09-3

Typeset, printed and bound by
F. Salvesen Bok- og Offsettrykkeri A/S, Mandal, Norway

All photographs by Nic Barlow except the photograph
of Matthew Manning's hands on the back-cover by Tim Booth.

Published by Eikstein Publications,
N-4532 Øyslebø, Norway

Contents

Acknowledgements

This book, and my life, would not be possible without listing heart-felt thanks to those who have supported me over the years. I would especially like to aknowledge and thank my parents, Derek and Valerie Manning for their wisdom and for always having given me the freedom of choice; to David Frost for over twenty years of support; to Tim Wheater for the music; to Graham Wilson for all the good times; to Shirley Hocking, my long-suffering secretary; to Lillian Takvam Nagell for all the good words; to Nic Barlow for his camera and deep friendship; to Mart Llewellyn for her kindness and inspiration; to Barbara and Walter Kraus for always being there for me and anchoring me, to my two wonderful children, Henrietta and Jethro, for showing me that sometimes children teach parents; and finally to Gig who has given me such love, unconditional support and the greatest happiness I will ever experience.

Matthew Manning, Suffolk 1995

1. Introduction

Matthew Manning: The man who takes the faith out of healing

Matthew Manning shot to fame in 1974 with the publication of his first book *The Link*. It created an international sensation and was published in 16 different languages, eventually selling one million copies.

The Link described the remarkable poltergeist activity that had occurred around Matthew since he was just eleven years old and told of the harrowing yet humorous consequences as he was twice suspended from the boarding school at which he was a pupil, was despatched to the psychiatric unit of a local hospital, and finally discovered that he could control the physical phenomena around him by producing the most remarkable *automatic drawings*. By focussing on the name of an artist he was able at will to produce superb drawings sufficiently in the style of that artist to fool even art critics.

In the same year Matthew had participated in a major series of tests at the New Horizons Research Foundation in Toronto, Canada, led by some of the world's leading scientists, including Britain's Nobel Prize-Winning physicist, Professor Brian Josephson. It was during these tests that psychiatrist Dr. Joel Whitton discovered that Matthew was producing a brain wave pattern never reported previously in anyone else; further tests showed that it was originating from a part of the brain which we all possess but which had, until that time, been believed to be dormant or inactive. It was the central, oldest and most primitive part of the brain, leading the researchers to speculate that perhaps Matthew's special gifts were something which we all at one time used but with the advent of technology were slowly lost. After the Toronto tests Professor Josephson stated:

"*I think we are on the verge of discoveries that may be extremely important for physics. We are dealing with a new kind of energy. This force must be subject to laws. I believe ordinary scientific investigation will tell us a lot about these psychic phenomena. They are mysterious, but no more mysterious that a lot of things in physics already.*"

"*In times past, respectable scientists would have nothing to do with it. Many of them still won't. I think the respectable scientists may find they have missed the boat.*"

When *The Link* was published a couple of months later, Britain's foremost television interviewer, David Frost, devoted an entire show to Matthew and his remarkable story. He was able to demonstrate some of his abilities on live television, leading one newspaper critic to write that "*David Frost, normally a wily interviewer, had been reduced to a gibbering jelly by a teenaged psychic.*"

The international attention also brought unwanted scrutiny from the British security ser-

Automatic drawings by Matthew in the style of wellknown artists.

Great Bores
of Today. *82.*

". . . You should have stayed up you missed this man on Russell Harty who has these fantastic psychic powers young Indian I think he was anyway Harty asked him to think of an object and draw it on a piece of paper and then put it in an envelope and the audience had to do their own drawings of what they thought he'd done and it was uncanny this bloke says there are thought waves like radio waves apparently ly which only some people can pick up and he's been working with scientists in America to try to discover what it is another thing this bloke can do is to do drawings exactly like Tom Keating it's as if he's possessed it makes you think doesn't it? I mean there are things that none of us can explain do you remember that time I woke up in the middle of the night when your sister's house was on fire hundreds of miles away. . ."

*From the British satirical magazine **Private Eye** a regular column reserved for people who are always in the news! It was published after Matthew's 1978 appearance on The Russel Harty Show on ITV.*

vices and Matthew was quizzed extensively by the late Lord Rothschild who, at the time, was head of Britain's security services.

In 1977 his follow-up book, *In the Minds of Millions*, was published. It described the remarkable occurences that had happened around the world as Matthew toured to promote *The Link*. An entire department store in Barcelona had been blacked-out while he signed copies of his book; when he appeared on Japanese TV, poltergeist phenomena had occured all over the country as viewers watched him demonstrate his ablilities; in Britain he had been approached by two Roman Catholic Archbishops as Pope John Paul VI lay dying.

However, in 1977, Matthew Manning turned his back on the sensational events that had made him almost a household figure in many countries. Driven by a powerful yet inexplicable experience high in the Himalayan mountains, he vowed only to become involved in research which might possibly have a positive benefit for others. For about five years he underwent extensive and rigorous testing at the Mind Science Foundation in San Antonio, Texas, at the University of California, and at London University. These tests produced the largest number of scientific reports on healing ever produced from the work of one individual subject as he demonstrated under laboratory conditions his ablility to influence the rate of degradation of human blood cells and enzymes, the growth rate of mould samples, the death rate of cancer cells, and the remote influencing of another person's brainwave patterns.

After the University of California tests, Dr. James Mishlove wrote: *"Our month-long experience with Matthew Manning has yielded sufficient evidence to refute the arguments of those who maintain that Manning is a fraud."*

A typical cartoon following Matthew's exploits in the early 1970's!

Matthew also demonstrated a quite remarkable ability to influence cancer cells in plastic containers during his tests in Texas. Dr. John Kmetz, one of the scientists involved, commented: *"The cancer cells were actually being killed by Matthew. In at least 60 per cent of the cases, the results were quite significant. When an individual who was not a healer tried to do the same thing, nothing happened."*

After years of undergoing various scientific tests, Matthew devoted all his time to treating the sick, with results often as impressive as those he achieved in laboratories. He has lectured and demonstrated all over the world, from Britain to Brazil, from Australia and Hong Kong to America.

Now acknowledged as the leading healer in Europe his services are sought by a wide cross-section of international society - from film stars and musicians, to politicians and royalty, as well as scores of ordinary people. He never claims miracles and is careful to explain that his abilities do not help everybody. He has also produced a wide range of highly acclaimed audio cassette tapes teaching how to help a variety of problems by learning simple relaxation techniques and programmes of attitudinal change. These recordings have been extensively used in hospitals and health centres throughout Britain.

He now devotes his time to treating clients during individual consultations at his home in Suffolk, and to leading seminars and workshops worldwide. Few who experience his energy at these events come away unchanged and there are countless records of people whose lives have been dramatically changed and healed through their participation in one of his seminars.

In Britain Matthew Manning has had the rare distinction of lecturing to the Oncology Section of the Royal Society of Medicine, and one medical practitioner has followed his work with patients very closely. Dr. Brian Roet, formerly of the Charing Cross Hospital in London, has written:

"Matthew Manning is an extraordinary young man. There is no doubt about that. I have seen many patients who have previously attended Matthew for healing; every one of them, without exception, has gained considerably from their meeting with him.

Sir David Frost and Matthew Manning

Matthew's openess and willingness to learn, combined with the special natural powers he possesses, make him a unique person in an area surrounded by suspicion and mystique.

*My many years training as a doctor and anaesthetist have taught me how much we do **not** know about the body and its healing processes. Matthew's powers are not discussed in medical textbooks, but I can verify their efficacy from those of his patients I have met."*

He also has a remarkable ability to be able to often visibly demonstrate his gift as he works with patients with, for example, restricted joint movements caused perhaps by arthritis. At his demonstrations he always invites a medical doctor or a physiotherapist to examine his chosen subject both before and after his healing treatment.

In March, 1995, Matthew again teamed-up with Sir David Frost to co-host a live television programme about psychic powers called *Beyond Belief*. Whilst the show was on air over 2.5 million people tried to call the television station, creating a collapse in part of the British Telecom system for several minutes. It was the greatest number of calls ever made to a Britsh television programme and the show was an instant hit attracting over 12 million viewers. It is now planned to turn it to a regular series.

Matthew successfully demonstrated his healing powers on *Beyond Belief* by working on four people at the same time easing years of pain and restricted movement for three of the four volunteers. The New Statesman commented,

"The only person with psychic powers worth bothering about was Matthew Manning, the acclaimed and proven healer. His contribution was quite miraculous."

I have now worked with Matthew for eight years, promoting his workshops and healing circles across Europe, and I have had a unique opportunity to gain an insight into his personality. I am deeply impressed by his warmth, humour, and human wisdom. From the years that I have spent with him I have learned that the healing energies described in this book have a far deeper impact on people than the obviously visible results in test tubes or on X-rays. Matthew channels an energy that leads everyone involved into a process of self-transformation not only on a physical, but also on an emotional and spiritual level.

I have also met many people who are today considered as *spiritual leaders* in our Western society and I can only confirm what many others who have met Matthew have expressed: that although being only just forty years old, he is a source of wisdom and inspiration that has healed and changed the lives of many people in a very profound and positive way. The crisis of our Western culture is deeply rooted in the loss of spiritual guidance and a rapid degeneration of human values which neither religion, politics, or science seem able to reverse. Matthew Manning is one of the very few people I consider to be able to lead us towards a healing of this situation. Both for myself and the thousands of others who have experienced Matthew's healing energy, the ultimate form of healing is best described when he says in his workshop,

"Heal yourself and the world around you will heal."

Walter Kraus (publisher)
Norway, April 1995

Chapter 2

Healing in the Laboratory

In May 1977, a month of experiments and tests had been arranged by the Washington Research Centre in San Francisco and a group of scientists from the Univerity of California at Davis. Jeffrey Mishlove, one of the leading researchers later wrote in their published report of the tests:

"Taken as a whole, our month-long experience with Matthew Manning has yielded sufficient evidence to refute the arguments of those who would maintain that Manning is a fraud."

One of the first experiments was conducted by James Hickman who had devised the simplest of tests, which if successful, would demonstrate an interesting healing effect. He had filled three test tubes with rye grass seeds; this particular variety was selected because it was known to grow quickly. On being given the first test tube, I was asked to try to influence the seeds for five minutes in order to increase the normal yield; with the second sample I was asked to exert an influence to decrease the yield, whilst a third sample had no contact with me whatsoever. The three test tubes of seeds were then given to a colleague of Hickman's who, not knowing which seeds had been influenced in which direction, transfered the seeds to new test tubes and randomly coded them, locking the code in a safe, before returning them to Hickman.

All groups of seeds were then planted out in identical containers and subjected to the same consistent environment whilst someone else watered each container on a daily basis with fifteen millilitres of ordinary tap water. James Hickman then counted

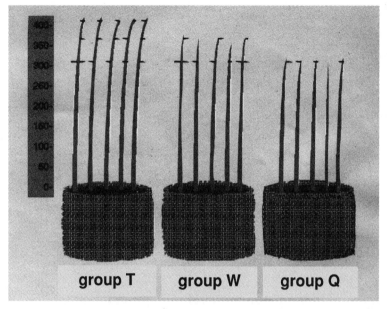

Figure 1: *Healing effect on the growth of rye seeds*
group T: influenced seeds in order to increase yield
group W: influenced seeds in order to decrease yield
group Q: not influenced

the number of sprouts and measured the weight of each plant on days 9, 10, and 11 after planting.

The results were intriguing! The seeds which had received healing grew significantly more than those with which I had no interaction. However, those rye grass seeds whose growth I had attempted to inhibit had grown almost at the same rate as those that I did not treat at all. It seemed therefore that I could promote the growth rate but was unable to slow it down.

"*A significant difference was observed in the comparsion of the total height of all plants in each pot between group T (in which Matthew tried to increase the plant yield) and group Q (with which Matthew did not interact), in the hypothesised direction,*" reported Hickman.

We then did the same experiment again but this time used radish seeds. During this trial I was merely asked to give healing treatment to a selection of seeds, whilst I had no contact with the second test tube. Once again, all the seeds were planted in identical boxes and were given equal water and light by an independent person who had no idea which seeds had been influenced and which were part of a control.

Twenty-three days after planting, James Hickman harvested, counted, weighed and tasted the results.

"Forty-two of the treated seeds sprouted compared with thirty-two from the control group. However, only thirty-two radishes from the treated group reached table size while twenty-nine of the control radishes were table size. The total weight of the treated plants was 187 grams compared with 152 grams on non-treated radish plants. More green foliage appeared to have grown above the treated radishes than the control group. There was no detectable difference in taste. These preliminary results indicate that Matthew's attempts to increase the yield was apparently successful."

If nothing else, this simple test did seem to confirm the old idea that some people really do have green fingers!

Several experiments, which perhaps had more potential for a healing in a practical sense were conducted by Professor Fred Lorenz of the Department of Animal Physiology at the University of California, Davis. One of the tests he devised certainly showed an interesting effect although it would not be the kind of experiment in which I would involve myself now!

It was an elaborate version of an experiment that is sometimes shown in biology classes at school. It involved stimulating a nerve in a piece of frog skin by minute electrical impulses created within the skin by chemical changes.

"Active transport of various substances across membranes is an important energy-consuming process, essential for pumping such substances against an osmotic gradient. Frog skin has an active sodium active-transport system," wrote Professor Lorenz.

It is possible to make the nerve jump by passing a mild electric current through it but my task was to try to make it react simply by mental influence. The skin had electrodes attached to it which in turn fed any information about changing electrical activity into a machine called a polygraph which then immediately produced a visual record on paper. If a straight line was drawn by the polygraph, it showed that there was no activity, but if there were sudden or sharp fluctuations, it indicated that the nerve was responding. I was to influence one piece of skin whilst David Deamer, a Professor of Zoology, who claimed no healing ability was to attempt to influence another.

"*The results of the single experiment were quite striking,*" Lorenz reported. "*Both Matthew and the control subject Dave Deamer attempted at first to increase and then to decrease the active transport*

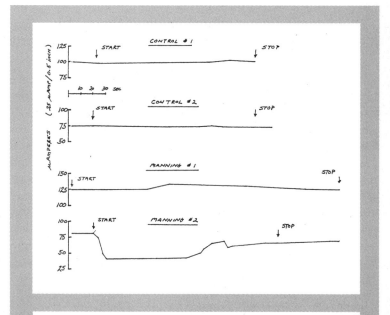

Figure 2: *Active transport of sodium through frog skin as affected by DD and MM. The upper curve by each operator showed the attempt to increase, and the lower curve to decrease, the rate of active transport*

current by holding the hands a few inches from the cell and sending psychic energy from the hands to it. When Matthew attempted to increase the active transport there was no change in the already high value of 125 microamps for one minute, followed by an increase of 8 microamps in 20 seconds and then a gradual decrease back to the original level."

"Matthew's attempt to decrease the active transport rate was cleaner and much more dramatic. Immediately after he started work the current began to fall and decreased from 80 microamps to 40 microamps in 10 seconds. This low level was maintained for a little over a minute and thereafter the current increased somewhat irregularly in spite of his continued effort, but had not regained its original level at the end of the run."

"In contrast, Dave Deamer's attempts had no effect on the active transport current."

Professor Lorenz and Professor Loring Chapman then conducted another successful experiment. The human brain is continually producing a complex fluctuation of electrical activity which can be picked up through electrodes placed on the scalp. Although they can only be crude indications of brain activity, their interpretation has, nevertheless, important clinical and experimental applications. A record of the brain's activity through electroencephalography can be used to detect and locate structual disease, such as tumours in the brain; it is also used in the diagnosis and management of epilepsy. Now though the scientists wanted to use the electroencephalogram (EEG) to assess the level of brain arousal during my attempts to influence volunteer subjects from a distance.

One of those subjects was Fred Lorenz himself who was some distance away from me in an isolation room. The results were startling.

"Following a baseline period, and responding to instructions from Dr. Chapman, Matthew sent (mental) suggestions to me to be wide awake, to go to sleep, to awake, to awake again, and to go to sleep, with rest periods between each. Dr. Chapman was able to see the effects of the suggestions in the EEG as it was being produced. I was very aware of being alerted three times, with drowsy or inattentive periods between, although I don't know if they were in exact temporal correspondence. My first remembered alerting was most dramatic and seemed to come out of deep drowsiness or even actual sleep."

"The correnspondence between Matthew's EEG and my own were most dramatic. These are most clearly illustrated by moments such as those where trains of high amplitude or slow waves are simultaneously evident from both heads. Especially interesting was a kappa rhythm which manifested simultaneously in both heads. The kappa rhythm is usually a sign of alerting during a drowsy state."

"The correspondence was not limited to such short-term and striking displays, however. It seemed that usually when Matthew was producing alpha rhythm, so was I. There were three consecutive pages of an awakened period, i.e. they cover 30 seconds of record, and during that half minute Matthew's record and mine shifted simultaneously from low amplitude, fast beta to irregular, slow waves and then to quite regular alpha. Such correspondences could be seen throughout the record and their validity is amply confirmed by computer analysis."

"During the initial baseline period, Matthew was producing a mixture of frequencies, while I settled down immediately into an almost pure low-frequency alpha rhythm on all channels. However, as soon as he tried to influence me, the respective EEG power spectra became more alike, and this tendency was maintained not only while I was awake and asleep, but also during interim rest periods. While being aroused, my low frequence rhythm was strikingly increased and the alpha (normally associated with rest and relaxation) was greatly decreased but not completely abolished. Meanwhile Matthew's low frequency rhythms were maintained, and his peaks in the alpha region were decreased even more than mine."

"When attempting to induce sleep, both the shift in pattern and the correspondence in the two heads were most striking. The low frequency rhythm was resumed in all monitored parts of my head; however, the frequency was increased from the previous 8 Hz to 10 Hz, an unusual shift rarely observed."

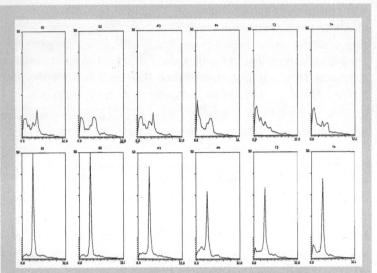

Figure 3: *EEG power spectra sampled during the initial baseline period. In figures 3 to 6 the top spectra are from MM and those below from the subject, F.W.Lorenz.*

"*Obviously, the similarity of Matthew's EEG and mine was greatly increased as soon as he started to try to influence me and was maintained throughout the experiment. Any further interpretation of these results may, however, be difficult. The presence of so much very low frequency activity in Matthew's EEG may pose a problem, as does its presence in mine during the altered state only. Its abrupt disappearance from both our heads both times I went to sleep is equally puzzling, although its actual absence from my EEG while asleep is not, because I wasn't allowed to sleep long enough to reach stage 4. However, the observed increase in alpha rhythms when I went to sleep seems to be a reversal of the usual pattern.*"

It was a clear demonstration that it was possible for someone to be physiologically influenced from one room to another. This was not based on a subjective judgement but was confirmed by

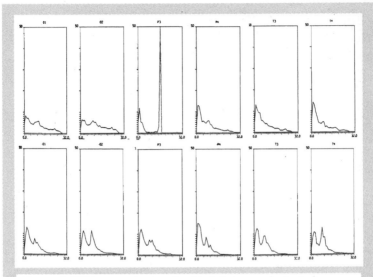

Figure 4: EEG power spectra: Sampled during awake periods.

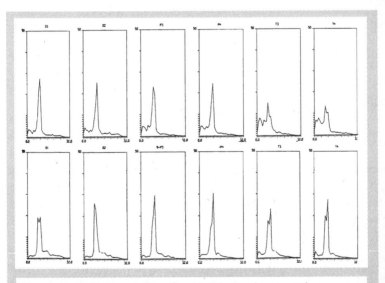

Figure 5: EEG power spectra: Sampled during sleep periods.

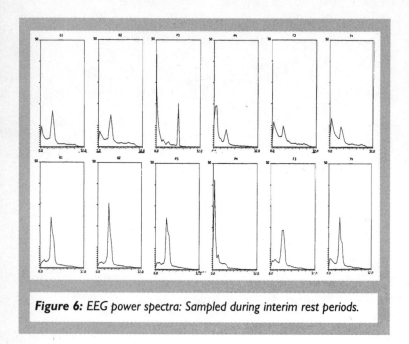

Figure 6: EEG power spectra: Sampled during interim rest periods.

analysis of our EEG records. Professor Lorenz was fascinated to know just what I had done; how had I managed to send him to sleep and then just as suddenly to have sharply awoken him at a distance?

Whilst trying to calm him, I had sat very still with my eyes closed, imagining him sleeping, becoming more relaxed, more at ease. I had not only imagined this, but had also tried to actually convey or project a sence of dowsiness through the wall. Not only had Fred Lorenz felt himself going to sleep, his brainwave records confirmed that indeed he had. When asked to arouse him, I imagined that I was running into his room shouting, "*Fire, fire*", as loudly as I could; I also tried to sense myself physically shaking him to get him to react. I chose fire because I felt that had an emotive quality that represents a primitive fear and it was visually easy for me to project. It certainly seemed to work quite dramatically!

In late 1977 I was invited to take part in series of tests at the Mind Science Foundation in San Antonio, Texas with a group of scientists led by Dr. William Braud. The results from these preliminary experiments were so impressive that I returned for several weeks early the following year. Numerous tests were carried out to see if I could influence from a distance the orientation of an electric knife-fish in an aquarium or the motor movement of a gerbil. Most of the experiments produced results which were statistically significant and all were later published in the Journal of the Society for Psychical Research.

However, there were two tests which provided very striking results and which showed it was clearly possible to demonstrate healing in a laboratory.

If human blood is mixed with water, the red blood cells quickly become stressed so that their surface membranes become permeable, allowing an escape of hemoglobin into the surrounding solution. This process is known as hemolysis. Visually it is like over-inflating a red ballon until eventually it bursts. If, however, the red blood cells are placed in saline solution, they will survive intact for long periods of time. Hemolysis can be monitored by measuring the amount of light transmitted through the blood-water solution. As hemolysis occurs, the solution's appearance changes from cloudy to clear, with a resulting increase in light transmittance. In this test I was to try to prevent the red blood cells from being broken down once they had been placed in water with only a very small saline content.

There was a sequence of five trials during which I was to exert a healing influence, and five trials during which for control purposes I removed my influence. The instructions as to what I was to do were based on the random order of ten cards shuffled twenty times; five of the cards would be blank and the other five would tell me to influence. During one of the trials I was placed in a distant room and had to influence the blood cells from 30 metres away. The scientists then accurately measured the extent to which the cells broke down by placing the test tubes in a machine, called a spectrophotometer, which measured the amount of light being transmitted through the solution. The more light that passed through, the more cells had broken up, and the less light that passed through, the less the cells had been injured.

This time the results, when analysed statistically, beat chance by odds of over 100,000 to 1. Most interestingly, it was found that the one trial where I influenced the blood cells from 30 metres away produced the greatest response! In his report Dr. Braud wrote:

"The major conclusion to be drawn from these experiments, of course, is that Matthew Manning was able to exert significant psycho-kinetic influence upon a variety of biological targets."

Although necessarily reserved and conservative when writing his scientific report, Braud was much more enthusiastic when talking about the series of tests to the Press.

"By concentrating his mind on the tube of blood, Matthew was able to slow down the death of the cells," said Dr. Braud, an experimental psychologist and former Professor of psychology at the University of Houston. *"Normally the blood cells would break down and die within a maximum of five minutes. But he was able to slow down the destruction so that the blood cells were still intact 20 minutes later,"* The National Enquirer reported in the United States.

The other remarkable results were achieved during an experiment with Dr. John Kmetz who had been doing research with what are known as Hela cervical cancer cells. These are a strain of cancer cells that were orginally taken from a human subject and which have been cultured and grown in laboratories for many years since their original removal. A great deal is known about their activity which is one reason that, apparently, they are widely used in cancer research around the world.

The cells are grown in a plastic flask, not unlike an empty audio cassette case, and they attach themselves to the inside surface of the flask with an electrostatic charge. This is the same principle that allows a rubber balloon, when inflated, to stick to the wall or ceiling if it has been rubbed against a woolen surface. The cancer cells grow in a layer, rather like a carpet, across the bottom of the flask and are submerged beneath a liquid protein on which they feed. If for any reason the cell is injured, if its metabolism is altered, or if it dies, the electrostatic charge on its outer surface is weakened or broken and the cell then detaches from the inside of the flask to float free in the liquid protein. At that point, to use the scientific jargon, it becomes *non-viable*. By removing a small sample of liquid protein from the flask and placing it in a spectrophotometer, it is possible to count the number of dead cancer cells in each millilitre of liquid.

The flask was then sealed with wax which would give a clear indication if I made any attempt to break into the flask physically. It was then given to me and it was my job, for twenty minutes, to attempt to heal the cancer cells so that the speed with which they detached themselves from the inside surface of the flask was accelerated. A second flask, which had also been earlier checked by Kmetz, was handed to a volunteer who claimed no ability to heal and whose job it was to copy and mimic all my physical movements; a third flask was left in a different part of the building and nobody interacted with it. In addition, all the trials were recorded on video tape.

During the first seven trials I was permitted to gently hold the flask between my hands (whilst the non-healer volunteer copied this action with their flask); on the eighth trial I was seated inside a shielded room and asked to concentrate on just one of three flasks that had been taped together and placed in Kmetz's office, the volunteer also doing the same; on the ninth trial I was still seated in the shielded room but was asked to concentrate on a nearby flask without touching it; during the thenth and eleventh trials I was in one shielded room whilst pairs of flasks were in a second shielded room; the twelfth trial had me sitting in the shielded room holding the flask whilst in the final, thirteenth trial, I was still in the shielded room but not permitted to touch the flask.

The results were the most dramatic that I had achieved in any experiments in Texas or at the University of California. It was observed that in all but two of the trials there was a marked increase in the number of detached, and therefore dead, cancer cells in the flasks on which I had been concentrating, yet by comparsion there were no changes in any of the flasks treated by the volunteer for control purposes. The number of dead cells had been increased in those successful trials by between 200% and 1,200%. This means, in simple terms, that if at the beginning of the trial there was just one dead cell per millilitre of liquid protein, after my healing there were anything between two and twelve dead cells in a corresponding volume.

One of the interesting features of this experiment was that I was still able to exert a very significant influence over the cells even if I was contained within a shielded room. This suggests that whatever was causing the healing was not electricity, magnetism, or electromagnetism as none of these forces could have penetrated outside the shielded room. The energy was also evidently highly directional because in the eighth trial, when I was to influence just one of three flasks taped together in a different room, that was exactly what happened. Only the one flask on which I had been focussing my energies showed any increase in the number of dead cells.

In the autumn of 1977 I flew to The New Horizons Research Foundation in Toronto to stay with Professor George Owen and his wife, Iris. It was the first time we had met since my previous stay in 1974 when I had also worked with Dr. Joel Whitton and Professor Brian Josephson.

Whilst I was staying with the Owens we were joined by a Detroit doctor, William Wolfson and his wife Tracy. One evening we were discussing the case of a remarkable American called Ted Serios who had the ability to project mental images onto a Polaroid film simply by concentrating on the camera. This idea rather appealed to me and I was particularly excited when George produced a Polaroid camera and several films. I was interested to see if I could do what Serios had done.

Tracy Wolfson took the camera and photographed me as I sat on a sofa in the Owen's study. I merely relaxed, looked at the camera, and made no attempt to do anything and it turned out a completely normal picture. (Picture 1)

Picture 1

Picture 2

Picture 3

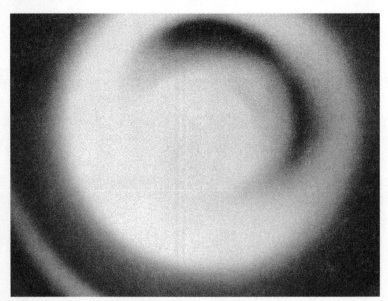

Picture 4

Picture 5

Picture 6

I then began to still myself and to meditate until I began to feel a tingling sensation, rather like mild electricity, in my hands. I held them up and told Tracy to photograph me. The photograph that appeared now showed what seemed to be a circle of mist forming around me. (Picture 2) A few moments later the sensation in my hands had intensified to a point where they were also feeling quite hot and, again, a photograph was taken. The result was dramatic and I could now hardly be seen behind white concentric rings of light that obscured virtually everything in the room. (Picture 3) Then the film ran out. A new roll was quickly inserted and the camera was pointed at me again.

This time, however, the trigger of the camera was not pressed and the shutter didn't open because I felt strongly that this time my energy had actually penetrated right through the shutter and lens directly onto the film behind. The resulting picture (Picture 4) showed again concentric circles of white light, even more intense than on the previous shot. As two different rolls of film had been used, it seemed unlikely that the film was faulty. It was decided however to use a second camera. Several rolls of film were used up without any apparent effect on any of the resulting photographs.

Later on, after a rest, I sat at George Owen's desk and, having briefly meditated, tried to imagine a large ball of light coming from my head. The photograph then taken by Tracy Wolfson with the second camera now showed just a ball, again surrounded by faint circles of light. (Picture 5) When it was suggested that I hold Iris Owen's hand, in an attempt to transfer the energy to her, we obtained another dramatic shot with the same ball of energy now clearly above her head. (Picture 6)

Perhaps this was the first time that healing energy was captured on film by an ordinary camera in such a dramatic way. The most interesting thing of all is to see the development of the energy from one frame to the next.

Having devoted considerable time to working with scientists from overseas, I felt it was only fair to also offer British researchers an opportunity to work with me. For a two-year period up until 1980 I was involved in a number of tests at Birkbeck College, University of London.

Professor John Hasted arranged a simple test in which I could try to influence the growth rate of mould samples grown on nutrient jelly in plastic Petri dishes. What were called *mucor* mould specimens were allowed to grow in a laboratory for about 24 hours, when their diameters were closely measured. Batches of eight were then made up and of these, four, randomly selected by blind choice of a technician, were kept out of my way as control samples, whilst the other four were given to me to influence for five minutes. It was my job to try to slow down the growth rate of the mould samples. I was allowed to touch the Petri dishes, but not to remove the lids. Immediately after exposure to me, the moulds were placed with the control moulds, and were left to develop. All the dishes were coded, with only the laboratory technician knowing which were which. Over a period of time eighteen seperate experiments were carried out with me. Later mathematical evaluation, after new measurements of all the mould samples had been taken, showed that the results beat chance by odds of several hundred to one and that "*various parts of it were of greater significance.*" This was mentioned because the first trial had produced an "*exeptional exposure after which an extremely unlikely retardation of growth rate occurred.*"

Another fascinating experiment was conducted at London University by Glen Rein, a Professor of Neurochemistry carrying out research at Queen Charlotte's Hospital in London. A few years earlier, neurochemists had found that human blood contains an enzyme known as monoamine oxidase, which is involved in metabolising certain critical chemicals in the brain called neurotransmitters. It was observed, for example, that certain migraine sufferers experienced a drop in this enzyme level shortly before experiencing a migraine although it was uncertain whether this caused the head pains or whether the onset of a migraine attack created the enzyme drop.

During experiments, samples of blood were taken from healthy male and female volunteers and the level of monoamine oxidase was then measured. The blood was then divided equally into two test tubes, one of which I was to influence whilst the other was similarly treated by a volunteer claiming no healing abilities. After five minutes of healing the enzyme level was measured again. The researchers did not know which sample I had treated and which was influenced by the non-healer volunteer.

The results, however, proved to be unpredictable because during some trials the enzyme activity was increased after my influence, whilst on other trials it decreased; on two other trials there was no change relative to the untreated blood cells. Evaluated statistically, the results beat chance by odds of several thousand to one. This unpredictability was what most confused Professor Rein because this particular enzyme would normally break down, yet on some of the trials it seemed that I not only prevented this process but also reversed it.

"*Although Matthew was asked to try to increase the activity of the enzyme, it is likely to be easier to cause a negative change in the direction the system is already going, i.e. to increase degradation,*" wrote Rein. "*It seems remarkable that this natural tendency could not only be stopped but also reversed, thereby causing an increase in activity.*"

"*The results are the first to successfully demonstrate a psychokinetic effect on an enzyme in its natural environment using a physiological substrate at both the cellular and subcellular level.*"

The implications of many of these tests are enormous. It should be possible to bring relaxation to a stressed person, to heal nerve damage and to perhaps help someone with cancer. If it is possible to affect in a test tube an enzyme that causes migraines, it should also give refief to a migraine sufferer.

I know that if I successfully heal somebody, a sceptic can always find an explanation and over the years I think I have heard them all! It's natural remission, it's placebo. It's psychological factors or it's faith. There must have been a wrong diagnosis is another common response. However, you cannot say that blood cells, cancer cells, frog nerves or enzymes in test tubes are influenced by placebo or psychological factors or faith!

When I gave up my involvement in laboratory testing by scientists in the early 1980's I felt it was more important to work with people rather than test tubes.

Chapter 3

The Healing Experience

The idea that healing only works if you believe in it is totally untrue. If faith had anything to do with it, I wouldn't have been able to get results in test tubes in laboratories. Healing will sometimes work superbly well on someone who is quite sceptical, and yet totally fail to work on someone who really believes in it. It also works on very young and brain-damaged children, as well as animals. Quite obviously it doesn't have much to do with a belief system.

Little Daniel Melton was just three month old when his mother Janice noticed something strange about his back; one side seemed to be sticking out more than the other. She took him to the doctor - nothing was found. She took him again when he was six months old. Again, nothing. She convinced herself that she was just being paranoid.

By the time Daniel was one, the deformity was too obvious to be ignored. In May 1988, Janice took him to Ipswich Hospital for an X-ray and was told that Daniel had extreme curvature of the spine. Doctors told her to take him to the Royal Orthopeadic Hospital, London, in September, for further X-rays. If there was no improvement at that stage, he would have to wear a plaster brace until he stopped growing.

Janice and her husband Dave were frantic. *"I couldn't stand the thought of my little baby in a cast until he was sixteen. What sort of life would he have?"* said 29-year-old Janice.

Janice was desperate and willing to try anything - including healing. She read an article about me, wrote and was delighted to receive an invitation to bring Daniel in for treatment.

For four months, Janice brought her son to me. She says: *"Matthew put on relaxing music and, while Daniel sat on my lap, he would put his hands over Daniel's back. He seemed instinctively to know where the problem was. He never actually touched Daniel, just laid his hands over him."*

When Janice and Daniel went back to hospital in September, the results of the X-rays showed that his back was almost normal. The doctors were very pleased. They told her to bring Daniel back in March 1990 to make sure the curvature had been completely corrected, but had to admit that he seemed cured.

Lorraine Baker's four-year-old daughter Natasha was fourteen months old when Lorraine went to her cot one morning and found her paralysed. *"She was like a rag doll. She couldn't speak or even lift her head off the pillow,"* said Lorraine of Hillingdon, Middlesex.

Although Natasha recovered the use of her upper body and voice within a week, she still couldn't move her legs and was eventually diagnosed as having transverse myelitis - an inflammation of a section of the spinal cord which prevented Natasha from moving her legs. The hospital was only able to offer her physiotherapy.

"I felt there must be something that could be done, and in February 1992, I took her to see Matthew. He put his hands on her back and within five minutes her legs started jumping around. We've been going once a month or so since then, and Natsha's condition has improved every time."

During one particular session I suddenly jumped as I passed my hands over her knees, it was as if an electric current had gone through me. The next day Natasha was able to pedal her bike, which she hadn't been able to do the day before.

Just before Christmas, she had four sessions with me over a two-day period and the following day she walked the length of the school hall during the nativity play all by herself. Her parents were absolutely thrilled.

Another remarkable story concerning a little girl, called Charlotte, suffering from progressive brain damage, showed astonishing results in different perspectives.

When I first treated her, back in 1989, she had extensive brain damage. Charlotte had lost all motor movement and couldn't walk, or use her arms and she was having difficulty swallowing.

She had already undergone extensive tests at Ormond Street Hospital and had numerous CAT scans showing that the damage was caused by a virus she had picked up from the cattle on her father's farm.

By the time the child first visited me, the doctors had given her a life expectancy of six to twelve months. It was one of those remarkable recoveries where, after about four sessions, Charlotte had returned completely to normal - in fact she's still like that today.

Her parents then took her back to Ormond Street where the doctors were so astonished they ran another CAT scan. They found that the brain damage was still there and the explanation they came up with - which I agree with in part - was that she had somehow re-routed all the signals through another, undamaged part of the brain.

Dan Hutchison had lost six stone and was suffering from extreme fatigue when he was diagnosed in 1984 as having cancer of the right adrenal gland which had infiltrated his liver. He said: "*Statistics showed that nobody with this form of cancer had survived and I was told to put my affairs in order. I went to see Matthew Manning twice a day. After the first visit I came out and saw that my daughter had tears streaming down her face. 'Dad' she said, 'you are carrying your walking stick'.*"

In 1992 Dan got a letter from the John Radcliffe Hospital, where he was originally diagnosed and which had sent him away telling him to put his affairs in order. He had never gone back to the hospital, and said he didn't want a scan or X-ray because if the tumour was still there he'd worry about it, if it wasn't then that was fine anyway. They invited him for an up-to-date scan, (he had shown up on their files as still being alive eight years after they had written him off,) and he accepted. They found that the tumour had completely gone and all that was left was just some scar tissue.

Sheila Lawler of South London was told by her doctors that she had an incurable cancer. Her troubles began in 1983 when cancer of the cervix was diagnosed. Radiotherapy seemed to have a positive effect, but six months later she developed cancer in the lining of her bladder. The doctors wanted to do a colostomy and remove the bladder and other parts.

Whilst Sheila was waiting in the hospital for an appointment with her doctor a friend showed her an article about me. She contacted me, got an appointment and received healing. After the healing session Sheila told me about her doctor's suggestion concerning the operation and asked me for advice. I told her that this decision had to be her's. "*That annoyed me,*" she said afterwards. "*Instead of advising me, my guru was telling me to make up my own mind. Yet Matthew must have sown a seed because after the healing I felt so well, so confident.*"

Sheila began questioning the surgeon about the operation and analysing his answers. He told her that the operation would be long and difficult. Her bladder and other major parts would be removed. Even then she would face many problems and indignities, but she would have between five and ten more years of life. Without the operation she could expect to live only another eighteen month or two years. But the quality of her life would be better. She would be spared the indignities.

"*I decided not to have the operation, and once I made up my mind I felt really elated. I believe Matthew gave me the strength for that decision,*" she said. The healing had a profound effect on her cancer. She has not been for hospital treatment since refusing the operation.

In 1983 Marguerite Otton's surgeon gave her six months to live after discovering secondary cancer, the result of removing a spot from her shoulder. So severe was it that he told her there was little point in offering her any treatment at all. The shock was enormous.

Years before she had had a masteotomy from which she had fully recovered. The sudden news that she had developed a new and virulent form of hormone cancer came as a total shock that left her very ill and led to weight loss and stomach pains. Marguerite was given hormone tablets but suffered so badly from side effects that she had to give up taking them. "*The surgeon said there was nothing he could do for me and I was sent away to die.*"

While in this state of great depression and fear, she then heard about me and came for regular healing sessions. "*He knew exactly where the pain was without being told. I could feel the burning of his hands and I had marks like sunburn on my back afterwards. I was always sick after the treatment - it was as if my body was physically ridding itself of the disease.*"

From the day of her first healing Marguerite found herself getting better and better. She put on weight and the pains in her stomach disappeared. She had no orthodox treatment since starting healing sessions.

She continues to occasionally see me though she has recovered from her cancer and also sees her surgeon. He remains amazed at her recovery, but is not able to offer any explanation.

Dan, Sheila and Marguerite all have something in common: all were given a short time to live, none had any orthodox treatment because of the advanced state of their disease, and all of them are alive, fit and well, more than ten years later. It also goes to show that the benefit of healing remains permanent.

Michael West, 49, from Winsford in Cheshire, first came to see me in 1988 suffering from bad osteoarthritis. "*I'd been a very active gymnast and swimmer before that and I also had two young children. Suddenly, I couldn't even climb the stairs, let alone go out to work,*" he said.

Michael was reluctant to try the gold injections and steroid treatment offered by the hospital, but admits he was deflated after his first visit to me. "*Matthew put his hands on my shoulder and knees and I felt this heat, but that was it. Then three days later the pain had gone, and after three weeks I had full mobility again. The hospital was amazed.*"

Michael said: "*At the beginning of 1992, I felt a slight twinge in my shoulder. I went to see Matthew, he put his hands on me and I've been fine since. I'm an open-minded person, but sceptical, too - no-one takes me for a ride. I believe that the healing ability is within every one of us, it's just that some are better at it than others.*"

Nicky Bilton, aged 37 reports: "*I had spent a year in excruciating pain from a gynecological problem. I was told that the only way the problem could be definitely diagnosed would be to have my womb removed and the tissues analysed.*"

"*By the time I decided to go and see Matthew, I had stopped work and was living in a fuzzy world, on prescribed pain killers and gin, which is a uterine relaxant. The first treatment was quite amazing. The feeling of heat was so intense that it was like being burnt alive from the inside and the searing sort of pain that accompanied it was an enormous relief. Then after each session, I just felt more and more relief. After six months I went back to work and after a year the pain had gone.*"

The Marquis of Tavistock suffered a loss of sight in his left eye after a stroke and suffered dysphasis, which is being unable to find the word you want.

His wife, the Marchioness of Tavistock, said: "*He did not believe in healing but went to Matthew after he helped a friend regain sight. Matthew put his hand on my hushand's head. He immediately felt warmth. And I felt it, too. After the first visit my husband looked incredibly peaceful and said he felt better.*"

"*After further sessions he regained 80 per cent vision in his left eye, which was the one worst affected by the stroke, and his dysphasis improved immensely. He is now a believer.*"

Elaine Carpenter, 36, a hypnotherapist, of Edwardstone, Suffolk said: "*I'd been trying to get pregnant for two years. When nothing happened tests showed I had fibroids the size of melons. I had these removed, but the operation left me with adhesions on both my ovaries.*"

"*I stopped ovulating and another fibroid was discovered. I was told there was very little chance I could become pregnant unless I had a further operation.*"

"*I booked in for the operation, but in the meantime decided to go and see Matthew. During the first visit, I felt warm and very peaceful and must have conceived almost immediately afterwards.*"

Dimitri Papalios, a Greek shipping owner living in London, believes that healing has saved him from years of agony.

"*For four years I suffered from cruelly painful cluster headaches,*" he said. "*They'd last from 30 minutes to 15 hours, though on average it was four hours. I'd curl up on the floor of a dark room and cry with pain. Or I'd sit for hours under a cold shower. That gave some relief.*"

Dimitri travelled all over the world searching for a treatment that would respond. But not even the famous Headache Centre in Miami could help him. Ulitmately Dimitri came for treatment with me. As a result his headaches have disappeared and his life has been "*revolutionised*", as he expressed it.

"*The headaches came at least once a day and all the specialists could offer were pills I could take for only two periods in a year for no longer than fifteen days at a time,*" he told the Sunday Express.

"*My first session with Matthew surprised me. I was wearing a thick jacket, but I felt heat from his hands burning right through it, it was like a blowtorch.*

"*I don't know what happened, but for three weeks after that I had no headaches. It was the longest gap I'd known for years without them. Then they came back, though less often and with reduced severity. I returned to Manning and then saw him once a month thereafter.*"

"*The results have been spectacular. Throughout 1987 I had half a dozen headaches, but they were so mild they were scarcely worth recording. And I have realised that relief from pain was only part of my cure.*"

"*The headaches were exacerbated by stress. I have always worked very hard. For a year I had only three hours sleep a night. Materialism was my major sickness, and Matthew cured it. He taught me to relax, to forge new standards. Once I'd go crazy over a small business setback. Now I can take disaster calmly.*"

"*Better still, I give myself time to enjoy my family. My wife, my children, the people in my office have all noticed the difference in me.*"

In February 1995 I received a remarkable letter from John Allison, a scientist who I met a month earlier when I treated his wife. He wrote:

"My wife Jane has just confirmed my feeling that I should write to you and describe what has happened. She had appointments with you last month, and she introduced me to you. You shook my hand firmly - I was very happy to meet you."

"That night, my right elbow and the adjacent parts of the arm ached unusually painfully, and the effect lasted a couple of days - but not enough to be a problem. I should mention that about twenty years ago I fell on sheet ice and hit my elbow, which, as a result, was slightly cracked or damaged in some way. Since then I have developed a small bone spur, which prevents my arm from complete, straight extension. The elbow would become painful for several hours if overstressed, e.g. by hammering or by digging and root cutting with a spade. Presumably this was a mild arthritis of the sort that develops when a joint is damaged or treated surgically. However, since our visit to Hartest, I have had no problem at all in the elbow, and I have been hammering and digging extensively! I can only attribute this remarkable improvement to you, and I must thank you for this pain relief - I'm sure I still have the spur, but it no longer troubles me."

"To me it definitely appears that the rest of us can be helped by your hand contact or near contact, quite possible unconsciously on your part. I mean there was neither any reason for you to suspect I had an injured elbow, nor may there have been any deliberated intention on your part to help me with a physical condition which was not giving me, at that time, any pain at all! Maybe this is a common occurence with your patients - it would not surprise me that your concentration aimed at a specific condition might actually spread out and benefit other problems the patient is experiencing. But I am surprised that the benefit spreads to auxiliary personnel - spouses such as myself in your waiting room!"

Occasionally in the course of one of my public demonstrations I will work with somebody with a hearing loss. It's possible to assess someone's level of hearing with, for example, a ticking watch. If at the start they cannot hear when it is pressed to their ear, and if after healing they can hear it from some distance away it is a reasonably good indication of improvement. At one well-attended demonstration I had asked for a volunteer with partial hearing; eight people all raised their hands. Rather than take just one person and leave the others disappointed I decided on the spur of the moment to take all eight and try an experiment.

Lining them all up on stage, having first checked their hearing levels, I then got them to all link hands together whilst I treated one gentleman on the end of the line. I had an idea that perhaps the healing energy would go straight down the line. After five minutes of treatment we discovered that that was just what happened!

In subsequent experiments during my workshops I discovered that I achieved even better results if I placed people in a circle rather than a line. I can only assume that this is because energy can escape from the end of a line whereas it recirculates in a circle. The majority of my healing work is now conducted by my working groups and the results are often as effective as working individually.

Inga Olsson participated in two healing circles in April 1994. Shortly before she came to the circles she had X-rays taken because she had terrible pain in her back. The X-rays showed a malignant tumour attached to her spine. After the healing circles she contacted me to tell about her reaction. Inga said that she felt filled with energy and when she arrived home and tried to turn on the light, all the fuses in the house blew. For no particular reason she felt very angry for a couple of days, but felt quite positive about it. To her it was like a cleansing, as if she was re-leasing something.

However, shortly after visiting the healing circles Inga had a bone-scan taken which showed that the tumour had totally gone.

I chose Elsa Nordhagen during a workshop in Norway for a healing demonstration. She had a frozen shoulder that was very painful and immovable and she had recently had an operation on her lower back which was causing great pain. Elsa had been driven to the workshop lying on the back seat of her husband's car.

She had also just contacted a private medical clinic to get further treatment that was unavailable at the hospital that carried out the original surgery. When the doctor called to tell her the results of the examination, she was recommended to have another back operation.

I chose her because it would be easy for the other participants to see if any change had taken place after the healing. The mobility of her shoulder and back were checked by a physiotherapist before and after the healing.

At the time I treated her I didn't know any more about her than that. After the healing she could move her arms freely and her back pain was much better. It was only then that she told me that scans taken at the clinic showed that she also had tumours in her abdomen. She was supposed to have had surgery two days before the workshop, but in order to participate she had asked for a postponement. She got that, but the doctors told her that she should not wait more than a few weeks before having the operation done.

The day after the workshop Elsa had an appointment with her doctor who did an ultrasound examination. He found that the largest tumour which had been seven centimeters across had shrunk.

The next week when she arrived at the hospital for surgery she remembered what I had told her after the healing session: *"Make sure that a new scan is made before the operation!"* So she asked for another ultrasound examination which the doctors did not want to bother with. She would not give in though, and finally the doctor, very irritated, agreed. He switched on the scanner and then switched it off again. He switched it on once more and seemed confused because he could not find anything. Another more senior doctor was called in, but neither of them were able to find the tumours. They then cancelled the operation.

She has been thoroughly checked by the hospital on a regular basis, and now three years later, she is still fit and healthy.

Belinda Moss, 35 years old, participated in a healing circle in Oslo in January 1994. She came in a wheelchair, accompanied by her young son.

Belinda developed problems with her pelvis whilst she was pregnant fourteen years ago and she had to stay in bed during all of her pregnancy. After giving birth she didn't recover as most women do after such pregnancy conditions. Belinda had had six operations trying to relieve her condition, and four years ago a metal plate was put in to strengthen her pelvis. This plate, however, had given her a lot of pain and spasms in one leg.

After the first healing circle she was completely free of pain for a few hours for the first time in many years. On the plane home to Bergen, the spasms went away and never returned. She felt something had changed dramatically. She suddenly felt like a different person.

After she arrived home she got a severe headache and vomited. She had to stay in bed for almost a week, but then she felt an enormous energy and felt better than ever.

Some months later Belinda came with her husband to a week-end workshop in Bergen, on a leave from the hospital where they had taken out the metal plate from her pelvis. She couldn't take full anaesthesia during the operation. To calm herself down she listened to a music tape I played during the first healing circle she participated in. She said that it was this music that got her through the operation. By listening to the music Belinda, in her mind, got back to the healing experience in the circle. She said that this kept the pain away, since the anaesthesia did not work as it was supposed to. At one time during the operation the tape recorder was taken away from her and then the pain was un-bearable.

After participating in two healing circles that weekend she felt ill again and vomited for some days. But then a wonderful feeling of having an enormous energy came back to her as had happened the first time. Belinda said that as she sat in the circle she was determined to get out of the wheelchair that she had been con-fined to for so many years.

Now she doesn't need the wheelchair any longer and is training hard to get back her strength. Her physiotherapist was very impressed and surprised at her remarkable recovery, because the operation report stated that she would never get out of the wheelchair. Belinda says that participating together with her husband in the workshop has given them both a better way of looking at life in many different and more positive ways.

Some people often like to think that healing is merely psychological or a hypnotic trick, but the results achieved on Tuire Huttunen, a lady from Helsinki, Finland, prove such ideas wrong.

Tuire, working as a nurse in a private clinic, participated in a one-day workshop in Helsinki in 1993. I chose her for a healing demonstration at the end of the workshop. She had rheumatoid arthritis and had great difficulties moving her wrist and neck and she was unable to bend her back. Before and after healing she was checked by a doctor. After 20 minutes of healing she was able to move her wrist, turn her neck and bend her back. Although she did not achieve a total freedom of movement, her situation was much improved. Later she told me that she did not need medication for a long time and the pain she had for years was gone, but came back after some months. She felt much better, but she was not totally well.

Later Tuire enrolled at a workshop in Stockholm on the 12th March 1995. Her doctor took a blood test two days before the seminar. After she returned to Helsinki a new blood test was taken on the 15th March. The sedimentation rate was 48 mm per hour before she left and 18 mm per hour after she returned. The same dramatic change occured on the hemoglobin level. On the 12th of March it was 100 which is quite normal for a rheumatic or an anaemic person, and five days later, after the workshop, it was up to 135. According to her doctor there is no medical treatment available that could make such a dramatic change happen.

After the healing in the workshop she was crying a lot. For her it seemed to be without any reason, but she believes it was part of her healing process. Now she is totally free of pain and doesn't need drugs anymore.

Natalie Soroy had read my book on self-healing and came to a healing circle. She had problems with an overactive thyroid gland. She was to have an operation. Natalie also had trouble with insomnia. She would wake up two or three times each night and laid awake for a long while before she fell asleep again.

Natalie cried a lot during the healing circle and had a quite strong reaction. After the circle she slept through the whole night and hadn't had anymore problems with her sleep there-after. When Natalie went to her doctor to have a final examination of her thyroid gland before the operation, the problem was gone and she didn't need the operation anymore. The doctors couldn't understand it and had no explanation for that what happened to her.

Some people go to my healing circles not only to get healed themselves, but also on the behalf of someone else. Inger Helset participated in a healing circle in Oslo. During the circle she was thinking of her husband who had been very much troubled by severe headaches for many years. She reported that after this healing circle her husband had no more headaches.

During a weekend workshop in Norway in 1993 I chose Eva Alveid for a healing demonstration. Eva is a nurse and had great problems with her neck and back due to lifting patients. After the healing the pain in her back was gone and she could move much more freely. After the workshop she grew better day by day. She told her doctors about the healing, but neither of them would accept this explanation for her recovery.

She made a lot of changes in her life after the healing. She changed her job to an easier one and focussed on her self-develop-ment. She had great difficulties in her relationship with her foster-mother, but a few weeks after the healing she managed to go and see her, and they resolved the problems. She said that this was a strong experience that has had great impact on her life. When she is feeling down or depressed she sits down and plays the music I used during her healing - then she can recall the feeling of light and warmth.

Lillian Takvam Nagell hardly knew who I was and what she could expect from healing. She is a lawyer and worked for the Norwegian Department of Justice before she was involved in a car accident which caused her a severe whip-lash injury confining her to bed for several months. She also had trouble with inflammation due to rheumatoid arthritis and now she could hardly move at all. She managed to get out of bed with only great difficulty, and had extremely restricted movements due to pain.

When she read an article about me and an advertisement that I was to give a workshop in Norway, she had already tried different treatments but none of them had very much effect. Lillian enrolled for the workshop and experienced a tremendous reaction after one of my healing circles on the second day.

"Matthew Manning went around the circle and touched everybody a short while. When he touched me, a very strong wave of energy washed through me, and I felt a deep peace and gratitude. I had had no expectations, so I was quite bewildered about my reactions," she said.

After the workshop she was collected by her husband because she was unable to drive herself. On the way home she cried for almost three hours. She told me later that her crying released very old tears and that this crying connected her back to her mother who had suddenly died of a brain tumour when Lillian was eighteen. This crying was very releasing for her and when she arrived home she felt very much at peace.

During the three days after the workshop her life was completely turned around. The day after the workshop she could see her life as if from a distance, in a detached way. She could see connections and patterns that she had not been aware of before. Two days after the workshop Lillian had got a new understanding of her life and could suddenly see meaning to it.

When she woke up on the third day, she was totally free of pain for the first time in many years, and she also felt an enormous joy of life. She found that she could move in such a way that the injured area between her shoulders was much more relaxed and the circulation was greatly improved.

The feeling of joy that Lillian experienced shortly after the healing was the starting point of a transformational process. She felt surrounded by a totally accepting love and was no longer afraid of dying. She believes that the latter was perhaps the most important to her in her healing process. All her life she had been afraid of all kinds of things. She was afraid of the dark, afraid of flying, afraid of illness and of death. But now Lillian wasn't afraid anymore. She felt safe and taken care of. Another remarkable result from the healing was that all her senses had been sharpened and intensified.

After some weeks this extraordinary feeling gradually disappeared and she got very distressed, wondering if she had done something wrong. But then she realised that the rest of the job was her own, and that there were many things in her life she had to deal with by herself. She realised that the healing had given her the tools to start working on herself.

Lillian explains: "*To me one of the most important things Matthew says is that you must have the willingness to confront yourself. To me this is about taking hold of the things you have suppressed and stored away. It can be a tough process sometimes. I can see I have only just started this work, but what has been of great help to me is that I have learned how important forgiveness is and to have trust in the process of life.*"

Chapter 4

Healing Ourselves

Most people now accept that what is called stress has a great deal to do with a wide variety of physical and emotional problems. There is a wealth of evidence to link the stress factor with heart disease, migraines, ulcers and even some forms of arthritis and cancer.

It is the most common factor in the history of many of the people that I treat. It's treatment is probably one of the most controversial within orthodox medicine.

We are all under some form of stress or strain. I don't believe it's possible to live without it and it is often said that the only person without stress is a dead one! But there is a difference between creative and constructive stress and destructive and immobilising stress.

The use of the word stress, as applied to human beings, was started in the 1930's by Canadian physiologist Professor Hans Seyle. Before that it was a word generally used by engineers. Seyle was involved in a research programme to study the hormonal function of rats.

During his experiments he would inject the animals with various toxic substances, and after they had died would dissect them to discover what physical changes had occured.

Regardless of what the rats had been injected with, Seyle found their tissue showed the same signs of damage. Their lymph nodes, which help to rid the body of outside invaders, such as infection or virus, had become wasted. They suffered from ulcers in the digestive tracts and they were very thin. Later he found that there were three stages of any prolonged negative stimuli.

What happened to Seyle's rats can also happen to us.

First there was an alarm reaction during which the body mobilised the necessary resources to deal with perceived threat or attack. He discovered that the adrenal glands, which manufacture the hormones to combat disease, came under heavy pressure at this time.

The second phase occured when the rat learned apparently to cope with the negative stimulus and its glands would produce sufficient hormones for it to recover. This adaption period, as Seyle called it, did not last forever. If the stimulus was maintained, the rat went into a sudden decline and died.

The human nervous system is designed in just the same way as that of animals. It's got two branches. There is the sympathetic which responds to an outer stimulus by producing the hormones we need to take action, and the parasympathetic, which is responsible for rest, digestion and restoring the hormone content of the body to a balanced state. What human beings tend to do is to undergo a stimulus or stress, which produces the hormone required for action, but don't or can't follow this up with the action or the necessary recuperation period.

Think how animals behave in the wild. They get hungry. They hunt. They eat and then they sleep. Professor Seyle concluded that there were two forms of stress: there is what he called eu-stress, which is the stress of winning or achievement and this brings about positive feelings. Dis-stress on the other hand, is the stress of losing, when we feel inadequate, insecure, helpless, despairing, disappointed. When we refer to stress we actually mean Seyle's dis-stress.

However, when stress is properly handled it provides the motivation to overcome the obstacles preventing us from reaching our hopes and goals. This is eu-stress. When it's permitted to run out of control it can lead to poor performance, illness and eventually death. This is dis-stress.

Stress need never become dis-stress, if you regard it's symptoms as an early warning sign which is there to make you aware of situations which threaten your well-being. Stress allows us to retire temporarily from a situation. It's a sign that we need to take a break.

The physical reaction to stress is what is known as fight-or-flight-syndrome. This means that hormones and chemicals are released into the body to help us fight or run away from the stressful situation. It's a throw-back to prehistoric times when it was a means of survival and therefore of crucial importance. Animals without this system would be calmly grazing whilst a predator approached. Understandably they didn't live long enough to think about fighting or running away.

As man evolved, he developed the same fight-or-flight-reaction to stress. However, the stressful situations in modern life are not created of predatory dinosaurs, and stress needs different ways of being tackled. The internal reactions which aid the fight-or-flight-syndrome are increased blood pressure, pulse rate, breathing, sweating and muscular tension, none of which have any outlet in our modern society. This process consequently places great strain on the body and mind. This stress-syndrome feeds on itself, because the more stressed we become the more tensed, anxious and worried we are. This produces stress in itself and subsequent physical or emotional problems.

There are many things that can cause stress. But it is important to understand that stress, like beauty, is in the eye of the beholder because what may cause you stress may not concern me - and vice verca.

Unfortunately there are many stresses common to most of us. We watch violence on television, often live in overcrowded circumstances and argue with the boss or our family. We may not have to contend with dinosaurs, but the modern day dinosaurs, the tax man or the bank manager are constantly with us. So we rarely find ourselves in a restful state. You may find yourself becoming anxious or irritable, you can't think straight and often suffer from headaches, sleeping problems or stomach upsets and in the longer term raised blood pressure or ulcers. A common response is to drink more or to smoke more or to take tranquillisers. But none of these actually take the stress away.

All they are doing is merely hiding the symptoms and allowing a temporary escape.

Basically, there are four typical signs of stress.

1. Being anxious and finding it difficult to relax. Actually anxiety can here be divided into two groups:

a) Anxiety learned from the past from others, usually parents, and incorporated into the system. This is known in medical terms as free-floating anxiety.

b) Specific anxiety, related to present day situations, such as coping with mortgages and traffic jams.

2. Becoming angry and irritatable when things don't go the way you want them to.

3. Worrying about things that worry won't help.

4. Experiencing difficulty in concentrating.

Change is the situation most likely to cause stress to us because it usually means some disruption of our relationships or stabilising influences in our life. Even minor change can cause considerable feelings of helplessness or hopelessness. It is your ability to adapt to change that is important. If you perceive a threat in your ability to cope with change, stress will occur and it therefore becomes a matter of positive or negative expectancy, more than anything else. We need to learn to be flexible in our attachment to other people, groups and goals and to be able to change radically and easily to other relationships when established ones are disrupted.

There is a list of questions that you can ask yourself in order to help cope with changes that you may have experienced in your life:

> • Know yourself, your feelings and attitudes.
>   What do you stand to gain or lose?
>
> • How can you help yourself to cope?
>
> • Know your new situation.
>   What does it involve?

- How should you behave?

- Can you try aspects of it out in advance?

- Know other people who can help by providing you with a sense of your own worth. Someone to talk to. Information. A perspective on your troubles.

- Learn from the past. How did this happen?

- Has anything like this happened before?

- If so, how did you and others cope?

- Look after yourself.

- You are the most imortant person you know.

- Keep fit. Eat sensibly.
  Talk positively to yourself.

- Let go of the past. What's done is done. Don't brood.
  Express your anger constructively.

- Set goals and make action plans.

- Decide what's best for you and work out how to do it.

- Think of alternatives.

- Look for the gains you've made.
  Think positively.

- What have you gained or learned?

I recommend four methods of relaxation and by relaxation I do not mean sitting slumped in front of the television or sleeping. It is a positive skill which has to be learned and practised regularly to achieve it's special effect upon the mind and body.

A short period of 10 to 20 minutes a day of proper relaxation has been shown to lower blood pressure, slow down the heart rate, overcome fatigue and improve concentration as well as releasing a variety of common symptoms which may be due to tension, such as backache and headaches.

Learning how to relax properly can benefit us all. Relaxation methods take time to learn and may take several weeks to work out but once mastered their beneficial effect increases.

The first method of relaxation I suggest is the mental imagary-technique. In your mind imagine a beautiful setting you would find relaxing. Sitting in a beautiful garden or taking a stroll by the sea as the sun sets.

The second method of relaxation involves correct breathing. The human body is remarkably adaptive and resilient. Human beings can survive for a long time without food and for several days without water. But without air, life ceases in only a matter of minutes. The fact is that every cell in our body needs a continual charge of oxygen in order to carry out a function properly. Our breathing supplies this energy to the bloodstream. Because it's been happening automatically for every moment of your life, you have probably given very little attention to it. - Think about your breathing. Anxiety is greatly increased if the breathing pattern is incorrect and just altering your breathing pattern may change you from a nervous wreck to a competent relaxed person.

A third form of relaxation is exercise. I don't think it really matters what kind of exercise you are doing, but I have often found that yoga is an exellent form of exercise. You may wonder why yoga rather than, say, jogging. The ancient practice of yoga, which originated centuries before Christ, is ideal for elderly people, and indeed, for those of any age who have some minor disability.

As we get older health problems may crop up, a painful hip, breathing difficulty, a heart-condition perhaps. Then we may be afraid to exercise in case we harm ourselves or aggravate the condition. There may be the feeling that we are generally stiffening up or are simply not as young as we were and really do not fancy all that vigorous leaping around that keep-fit-exercises seem to involve. Yoga works so well because it's slow, smooth movement can be adapted to every individual. If your arm will only lift to shoulder height you work at that level. There is time to find the fine line between effort and strain, without a sense of competition or the feeling you have to keep up. Yoga is more than physical exercise because good classes still include attention to posture and breathing.

Perhaps the best form of relaxation is laughter! Recent research has shown that people who can laugh at themselves can cope with obstacles far more effectively and rebound more quickly than those who simply cannot smile at misfortune. An American councellor, Harvey Mendez, specialises in the use of humour as a healing tool and believes that humour is a very great coping mechanism. When a client is very anxious about something he tries to encourage them to break out of their anger and fear by laughing at themselves. The advantage of humour is that you can release a lot of repressed thoughts that perhaps normally you would not have had the chance to express. Those who keep their sense of humour can deal with more of life's problems and release pent-up tension in a pleasant way.

According to one French doctor, Pierre Dachet, laughter can deepen breathing, expand blood vessels, improve circulation, accelerate tissue healing, and stabilise many body functions. In short, it acts like a powerful drug. It has been noted by some French researchers, who termed laughter *stationary jogging*, that those who laugh a lot are less prone to digestive disorders and stomach ulcers. New research shows that a good hearty laugh acts like a mini-workout, reving up the cardio-vascular, respiratory and nervous systems, according to Dr. William Frey, an American researcher from Stanford University School of Medicine. The latest study suggests that laughter may also be a physical release and that the increase in heart and blood pressure rates and the muscle vibration induced by laughing are often followed by a feeling of enhanced relaxation.

If you have been in the habit of ignoring or supressing minor ailments, many of the ideas I have just given to you may come as quite a new concept. Remember that what perhaps starts as disordered function can develop into physical disease. So, attending to stress can be true prevention.

It may surprise you to learn that people often decide when to be ill. It's been found that 90% of the population experiences some symptom of illness in any two-week period. Further studies have shown that the decision whether or not to seek medical advice for these symptoms is strongly influenced by social and psychological factors.

A research study completed in 1979 showed for example that colds are more likely to strike an introverted person who has allowed the stresses of life to interfere with their social life and their work. I find that there are almost as many different reasons for people developing illness as people themselves. There are some illness-triggering mechanisms which seem more prevalent than others, and interestingly, many seem to stem from childhood.

Children will often learn, if they have a test at school for which they have not done their homework that there is a very simple way out of it. They tell their mother that they have a sore throat and they are kept at home for the day. The patterning has been learned and stored from an early age. If, later in life, that same person is involved in a boring and unsatisfactory job, illness may be a legitimate escape route. Maybe when you were a child, a younger brother or sister appeared on the scene and you believed that your parent's love and attention had been switched to this younger sibling. But, when you were ill in bed with measles your mother suddenly seemed to give you much more love and care. You learned that there is a connection between being ill and gaining sympathy or love.

Is your illness perhaps a means of getting you out of a job or a situation you cannot avoid in any other way? Does it shift a balance in a relationship perhaps by altering someone else's attitude or behaviour towards you? Does it in some way strengthen a relationship?

People who are self employed may feel that they have much greater control of their lives, but for the person employed by a large company with little or no job satisfaction and no feeling of involvement in an end-product, illness may be a effective means of asserting control over events.

Both unemployment and retirement can bring problems too, because being out of work can cause more problems than little or no job-satisfaction. A recent study showed that redundancy or the threat of it resulted in a 20% increase in the number of consultations with GP's by workers and their families, and a 60% rise in hospital visits. It was also found that there was an 11% increase in illness when jobs where insecure or lost, compared with a 9% decrease amongst workers in other local firms who had secure jobs. Results suggested that the threat of redundancy is a stress which is equal to, if not greater than, the actual event.

I believe that major change in life-style can frequently lead to major illness. In 1981, a team of researchers at London's Westminster Hospital discovered that people with rheumatoid arthritis had suffered their first attack of the disease not long after a major upset in their life such as bereavement, divorce or job loss. Like other doctors who have looked for possible psycho-somatic factors in rheumatoid arthritis, they also found that patients often came from families where the mother was a tyrannical figure - hard to love but difficult to break away from.

The evidence to link emotional stress with heart-disease is much stronger. Two American cardiologists, Maya Friedmann and Ray Rosemann, studied a group of accountants through a six-month-period. They were asked to keep a very careful record of what they ate in order to determine whether a food-factor affected their hearts. As April, the busiest time of the year for accountants approached, their cholesterol level rose sharply even though their diets had not changed. Once the April deadline for tax returns had passed and their work load was reduced their cholesterol levels dropped too.

We all have the ability to choose a more positive alternative instead of self-destructive attitudes. Learn not to project your past experiences of pain into the future, or you spend the rest of your life haunted with fear; fear of emotions, mistakes, success, failure, other people, weakness or rejection, maybe even fear of yourself. There is only one time that is important, and that is now.

You can spend the rest of life looking backwards, worrying about the future and miss the present. You may not be able to change past events but you can change your thoughts, emotions and attitudes towards them. For me that is where true healing really begins.

My approach relies on reversing negative psychological and emotional trends, encouraging people not to feel trapped and victimized by life and to deal with problems in a positive and creative way. I like to use goal-setting to help to re-establish a connection with life. This represents a re-commitment to life and the body's defences respond to feelings of hope by taking up the fight against illness.

Some people though would rather die than re-commit themselves to life. But why should they find death preferable to life? Often it's because they never discovered their own identity or lived their own life which can eventually bring about a state of hopelessness that expresses itself in a life-threatening illness. Hopelessness will often stem from a lifetime habit of pleasing others rather than living one's own life. When pleasing others becomes such a burden and so far from what one really wanted to do in life, death becomes preferable.

Attitudinal healing's founder is Dr. Gerry Jampolski, a psychiatrist who has mainly worked with children with cancer. He has achieved remarkable results with alternative healing methods. It was while Jampolski was working as a student doctor in Boston in 1949 that he first became interested in cancer and the will to live and the will to die, and learned that through hypnotic suggestions a wart could be made to disappear. It was on this basis that he realised that through mental imagary and suggestion one could rid oneself of pain and change perception and illusion of illness - that in fact, there was nothing the mind could not do.

When we think someone is angry and attacking us we choose in attitudinal healing to see that person not as attacking us but just being scared. We learn in extending our love to others and helping others with no expectation of anything in return, we also help ourself. As we focus on other's fears and problems, our own seem to dissolve and peace of mind prevails.

There are ten areas where you are most likely to encounter a negativity entering your life. By observing and changing these negative areas into positive ones you can instigate new perspectives in situations that will ultimately benefit your health and happiness. The following points may help you in this way.

1 - Think well of yourself and your accomplishments and take the opportunity to re-affirm these regularly. Remember, the basis of being able to love and respect anyone else is to first learn to love and value your own self.

2 - Rather than worry or complain about what you do not have, appreciate what you do have. Remember, we get what we need in life not always what we want.

3 - Surround yourself with beauty and light inwardly and outwardly. Your environment is external but your spirit is internal and eternal.

4 - Do not allow another person's criticism to affect you. Have faith in yourself and your ability. Remember, criticism is also another way of expressing jealousy and often appears in those who lack confidence and self-worth. The unhappy and troubled person can also be critical.

5 - Accept each circumstance as an opportunity for growth and self-improvement. We learn from experience, whether good or bad.

6 - Remember that every cloud has a silver lining. Even negative life events have a reason for happening. All events in life come as part of the learning process.

7 - Leave yesterday's sadness behind you and look forward to tomorrow with hope and joy. Why worry over a past event that you have no means in the present of changing. Let it go.

8 - We all make mistakes. Don't fret over what is too late to change. Store it in your bank of experience. Yesterday's mistake can become tomorrow's triumph.

9 - Though you may still want it, let go of what you no longer need. Let the outworn go so that you can be open and receptive to new circumstances.

10 - We all shelter under the same umbrella of universal consciousness. Francis Thompson said:

All things by immortal power
near or far
hidden to each other
linked
are.
Thus we canst not stir a flower
without the troubling of a star.

Learn that you are free - free to question, feel, think, choose, communicate, change, assert, accept, forgive, release, know, be, live, and love.

It often comes as a surprise to people to be told that they *can* take charge of the way that they think. We are brought up with the idea that pills and injections from outside can cure physical illnesses; there ought to be something equally easy to cure emotional ones. We are also brought up with the feeling that we are the victims of the unpleasant thoughts and emotions that just arrive in our heads. This is made worse when what we think or feel is unacceptable to other people, who tell us that we shouldn't feel like that, we should pull ourselves together. That is not what I mean by positive thinking. Often somebody cannot snap out of their negativity that easily, and whilst trying to pull themselves together by pushing aside unpleasant thoughts they merely repress these thoughts, only to have them emerge again later on, adding to their feeling of helplessness.

Some of my paitents have what psychologists call a poor self-image. They are always running themselves down; they always think the worst of themselves; any compliment they receive is quickly rejected. In short they are their own worst enemy.

So how can you think positively, and how does it work? The first thing is to realize that your brain and the thoughts it produces are not your whole self. The brain can in fact be regarded as an excellent computer into which all kinds of information have been programmed from your birth onwards by parents, teachers, society, advertising and the media. Because it is *your* brain inside *your* head, it feels like *you*, and what it thinks feels real and truthful to you. If your computer-brain tells you that you are a worth-less person you will probably agree with it, and thus add to the store of negative information which may have nothing to do with actual reality at all.

You are not a computer, or a set of conditioned reflexes; you are a human being who was given that computer to serve you, not to control you. Once you begin to see what is happening you can start to change that computer programme. You can decide right now that the next time you find yourself thinking something negative about yourself, you will replace that thought with something positive. That may sound simple, but it really does work. Each time you choose to think a positive thought you are re-educating your computer-brain.

There is, however, a world of difference between positive thinking and self-deception. Positive thinking does not mean trying to fool yourself that everything is fine when it is not. Let us take an imaginary example. I may have a patient who comes for healing because of a breast tumour. After talking to her I discover that the young woman concerned is unhappy because she has no boyfriend and is unmarried. She may well have been fed a programme by her mother, friends or the media that women are only worth something if they have a man in their lives, and as long as she continues to believe that she will go on feeling worthless and depressed. Once she can recognize that her belief is simply an old tape that has got stuck, she can replace it with something more positive. It is here that she must be realistic. It is no good if she tries thinking, "*Next week I'm going to meet the man of my dreams,*" as she is likely to be disappointed. The positive thought in this situation would be, "*I am worthwhile whether I am alone or not.*" This will have several effects. As with any positive affirmation it will break the circuit of negative thinking into which she has been trapped; it will call a halt to the production of damaging stress hormones caused by her anxiety, and the more she thinks it, the more she will *feel* like a worthwhile person. Something may well then happen that often occurs when people make this kind of change in their thinking. Having learned to value herself and lose her anxiety, the tumour begins to regress and the right partner may well appear in her life.

For too many people their thoughts are more like a stream of constant self-criticism that they may not be fully aware of. Try listening to what you are telling yourself because once you can hear what you are saying you can start contradicting it. There is a remarkably simple exercise which can quickly change negative self-beliefs to positive ones. Make two lists of beliefs that you have about yourself: one of negative beliefs and one of positive beliefs. When my patients have carried out this simple exercise they often find that the positive list only contains three or four items whilst the negative list covers sheet after sheet! Have an objective look at the negative ones and ask yourself whether they are really founded in fact. They may seem to be simply because you have been listening too well to the tape playing in your brain. I remember a young man who brought me his lists; one of his negative beliefs was, "*I am no good at making friends.*" I crossed it out and by changing a few words placed it on his positive list. "*I am willing to make more friends*" I wrote for him. The situation may be the same for the moment but at least he is giving himself a totally different message about it rather than acting on his old belief as though it were an instruction.

When you have gone right through the negative list, changing each entry to positive beliefs, wherever possible tear-up or throw away the negative list. You have listened to your own self-criticism for long enough. Make several copies of the new list of positive self-beliefs and pin it all over your home so that whichever room you are in you will see it and reinforce it.

There is an extremely useful book by Cherry Boone O'Neill entitled *Starving for Attention*. The author, a young woman, is a daughter of the famous American singer Pat Boone, and the book is an account of how she overcame the slimmer's disease, anorexia nervosa, by using self-healing techniques. She describes how she was not only refusing to eat properly but also taking overdoses of laxatives in her attempt to lose weight. After a number of massive overdoses she was hospitalized and very nearly died. She was kept in hospital so that she could be encouraged to eat properly and not later induce vomiting to lose it again. After several weeks in hospital she was barely any heavier than when she was first admitted because, although she would eat meals under the watchful eye of nursing staff, she would then ask to go to the toilet where she was not supervised. Sticking her fingers down her throat she would return all the food. She makes an important point in her book: the doctors treating her never asked why she was doing it. They were treating symptoms and not the root cause. Her life was eventually saved with the intervention of a psychologist, Ronald Vath.

Vath's first question was why was she starving herself. With the help of his counselling it soon became apparent that there were two fundamental causes. The first was that for all her life she had lived in the shadow of her famous father and had developed a poor self-image. She was never Cherry Boone, she explained. She had always been known as *Pat Boone's daughter*. It always seemed to her that everyone's attention, time and love was devoted to her father whilst her own emotional needs were not fulfilled. She began to starve herself literally, but unconsciously, to gain attention. The second factor was that from an early age she had been encouraged to follow in her fathers's footsteps and she had been thrust into his TV shows. Her parents wanted her to sing and dance and she was quite happy to do so for some time. During her teenage years she became aware of the images of apparent female perfection presented in advertisements in women's glossy magazines. Comparing herself against these other images she decided she was too fat and began to exercise and diet. Tragically she lost control and developed anorexia.

Ronald Vath used the positive/negative beliefs technique as one of his tools for self-healing with Cherry Boone. She describes how she had no idea that she had developed such a poor self-image; almost everything she believed about herself was negative. She spent several days transforming her negative beliefs into positive ones which she pinned all over her apartment. Additionally, her husband reinforced by telling her positive things about herself every hour for several days. She recovered and later wrote a book of her experience.

It may not be easy at first and you may not believe the positive things you are telling yourself. Don't worry about that. It may take a while to reprogramme your brain. Treat it as an exercise, a new skill to be learned, even a game. Do not expect to succeed the whole time, or you will simply find another reason for criticizing yourself when you fail. But if you take, say, five minutes in every hour thinking positive thoughts, you will be taking a major step in turning around the whole pattern of your thinking.

Once you begin to see that you *can* change your thoughts you will perhaps start to see that a whole number of things that had been damaging your health can be viewed in a different way. Facts are facts, but you have a choice about how you interpret them. Once you can see that, a whole new world of freedom lies ahead of you.

Occasionally the cause of illness in one of my patients may not be very specific. Rather, they have a general feeling that there is something wrong with life; perhaps it has not turned out the way they thought it would when they were young; or perhaps, if they are young, it is not the way they think it *should* be: full of fun, love, success and excitement. People are not helped by the fact that the media, films, television and especially advertising often present some sort of ideal life that we all ought to be enjoying. If you look at the real world you will see that very few people are living *ideal* lives. But the happiest people are those who maybe recognize that life is not always perfect and that they are responsible for their own happiness and do not take it personally when things are unsatisfactory.

Comparing life as you think it ought to be with life as it really is and blaming yourself or others when things do not fit in with your ideal is quite a good way of getting depressed. Some of the people will say "*This would never have happened if my daughter hadn't married that dreadful boy*". Blame never helps any situation or solves any problems so it is best to forget about it. Have a look at the situation, whatever it is, and see if you cannot find another way of looking at it. Perhaps the husband or wife that you feel is neglecting you just as badly needs your love and attention. Perhaps you have decided that you are a failure because you have not passed an exam or you have not been chosen for promotion. Try giving yourself a different message. That exam or loss of promotion was an experience from which you can learn; you can look at that one failure as a springboard from which you can bounce back, rather than a steamroller that has flattened your ego.

I find that a number of very sensitive people, especially youngsters, feel that it is difficult to be positive about anything because of the situation of the world as a whole. *"How can we think positively when there are starving people, when people are killing one another, and the planet is being polluted?"* they ask. They feel they cannot look forward to a future because there may not *be* a future.

I believe that each of us can contribute to the future of the world. Indeed everyone of us is doing so at each moment of the day whether or not we are aware of it. We are not seperate from the rest of the world, we are a part of it. We are the trees that make up the forest, and the health of the forest depends upon the health of each individual tree. We can contribute to the peace of the world by learning to experience peace within ourselves. I do not mean that we should close our eyes and escape into meditation but rather that the person who is healthy, happy and clear-minded will have much more to contribute to the peace of the world than people who are bogged down by negative thinking. If each one of us can create more love in ourselves and the environment, then it will be possible for the amount of love in the world to outweigh all the hatred, greed and selfishness that affects so many people's health. But to make that happen, we have to start with ourselves.

Sigmund Freud said many years ago: *"In the final analysis, we must love in order not to fall ill."* This, I am convinced, is a root cause of much of the disease that I treat. What Freud told us all those years ago is now being demonstrated scientifically. Researchers on both sides of the Atlantic are finding that romance is perhaps the best antidote to the common cold. Dr David McCleland, of Boston University, studied one-hundred people, aged eighteen to sixty, to prove the point. He says, *"Dwelling on the positive experiences of loving or being loved appears to raise an individual's concentration of immunoglobulin."* That stubstance, according to many scientists, is the body's first line of defence against chest infection. Dr McCleland found the substance increased substantially in most people who watched a film about Mother Teresa. Blood samples also showed an increase in T-cells, which combat viruses.

Virologists at Ohio State University found that happily married women have stronger immune systems than women whose marriages have turned sour. Women who have been separated from their husbands for a year or more had less immunity to disease than those who were happily married.

People everywhere are looking for love, feeling sad and rejected when they do not get it. The trouble is that most people are looking for love to come from outside themselves. If as a child you felt loved, you are most likely to feel comfortable expressing your feelings. However, if you felt unloved, you feel threatened and fearful about expressing your innermost feeling, and for protection will bottle them up. Furthermore, if you perceive that one of your parents doesn't love you, in your childlike mind you assume responsibility for this condition by condemning yourself as being unlovable. To compensate for this perceived lack of love, you try to earn love from your parents and peers by pleasing them, a strategy which then gets projected onto all your other relationships. This is why cancer patients, for example, are often *too good to be true*. Their accommodating, helpful behaviour says, *Please love and accept me*. Yet our ability to love can only come from within: the best way to put more love into our lives is to start giving love, and the best place to start is by learning to love ourselves.

There is a traditional Buddhist meditation practice often called *Loving Kindness, Loving Awareness*, which I sometimes use during my seminars. Its aim is to experience aspects of love: to love oneself and friends and enemies alike, so creating a global unity. It is a simple exercise which you can easily practise by yourself. Find a comfortable position in which to sit and gently close your eyes.

Some of my patients have had problems during their early years: the death of a parent, a divorce, lack of love or too much criticism from one parent or both. Some people live out their

1. Focus and experience loving yourself. Look at yourself and bring into mind Love and what it means in relation to your own self. Be aware of any associated feelings, impressions, associations, images, or perhaps colours.

2. Focus on love for someone to whom you already feel a close bond. How does love appear in this case? Once more note any associated ideas or feelings.

3. Take as an object of your love a neutral person, someone towards whom you have no particularly strong feelings - someone you feel indifferent to. Once more note any associated ideas or feelings.

4. Now focus on a person you dislike or even feel hatred for; someone who brings about very negative feelings. Extend your love to them.

5. Bring all these together now and extend the same feelings of love toward all.

6. The above now moves out to extending love to people in the same room, street, town, country, globally - until the whole earth is surrounded and engulfed by whatever you perceive your own image of love to be.

lives looking for the love they did not get as children. Sometimes they also carry around a burden of hatred and resentment towards their parents or the people who have hurt them. It is these feelings which have so often been turned inward against themselves to cause illness. If this is similar to your situation, what can you do about it? Of course, you cannot go back and have your parents do it all over again. What you can do is to start giving *yourself* the love now that you did not receive then. Again, this is something you will need to learn and practise.

There is a very effective exercise which will help you to release and transmute some of these negative feelings. You will need a partner for this exercise. Sit opposite each other, making direct eye contact, but there should be no verbal communication.

1. Look at your partner and imagine that the other person really likes you. They think you are a nice, kind, loving person and are really happy to be with you. Be aware of any thoughts, feelings, symbols, or bodily reactions that occur and examine them.

2. Imagine that your partner really dislikes you. They are criticizing you and looking at you with scorn and hate. Examine what you feel and think now.

3. Imagine your partner is now someone from whom you can learn. See him/her as being an instrument in your growth. Examine how that feels.

4. Imagine the partner to be another soul, a human living being, a fount of unconditional love, someone whom you can accept without condition and vice versa.

At the end of the exercise discuss with your partner your reactions and feelings to each command. Examine, experience and learn from each other how this felt, to be sitting with someone who either loved or disliked you.

It may help if you recognize that a part of you is still an unloved child. Be kind to yourself, as you would be to that child. Encourage and praise yourself, and do not nag yourself if you do not come up to your own expectations. Treat yourself as you would like to have been treated as a child. You can even imagine yourself doing this by seeing yourself as a child and telling that child that *you* love it and want to take care of it.

If you have been through an unhappy or painful childhood or relationship, it does not mean that you have got to be unhappy now. So many people remain locked in the past by continually reliving the events that caused them pain. Tell yourself that your past is not happening to you *now*, unless you are recreating it for yourself. Accept that that is how things happened, and no amount of brooding is going to alter that.

Erin Pizzey, the well-known writer, established a hostel in London for battered wives. She discovered that many of the women who sought refuge after having been beaten up by their spouse or partner had something in common. As children they had been beaten up by their fathers. This again illustrates the way in which people relive the past by projecting it into the present.

If you have suffered a great deal of emotional pain and hurt in the past, you may well be carrying around a heavy burden of anger and resentment against those who hurt you. Sometimes these feelings may have turned into anger and hatred against yourself - self-hatred, for example, is a common cause and symptom of depression. Let it go. Remember that the resentment you feel is producing harmful chemicals in your body and is probably affecting your view of the world as a whole. It will not alter the past one little bit.

Make a decision to release yourself from the past. If you can, forgive the people who have hurt you. They were probably unhappy and confused themselves. By forgiving others, you are helping to heal yourself, and you are also creating space in your life for more positive helpful people to come in. If the word *forgive* is difficult for you to accept, then simply think of releasing yourself and breaking the links that tie you to those who hurt you. You can imagine your own pain and anger leaving you like a black cloud and floating away into the distance, getting smaller and smaller until they evaporate into the sky.

You can imagine the people you are angry with, and tell them that you forgive them and let them go. Do not imagine yourself hurting them but let them walk away to a distant place where they will be happy and out of your life. You may not initially *feel* forgiving; what is important is your willingness to forgive. You may also need to forgive yourself. Whether you have actually done something that you really regret, and there are very few people who have not, or whether you suffer from that overall sense of guilt that so many people seem to be burdened with, feeling guilty will not put anything right. Remember the child within you who is still growing and learning and is bound to make mistakes. Allow yourself to be imperfect, let the mistakes go, forgive yourself and love yourself.

There is another exercise which looks at ways of dealing with such emotions as fear, anger, jealousy, hurt, sadness, guilt, etc.:

Sit and close your eyes and get in touch with your own body. Now remember a situation in which you felt one of the above emotions (hurt, anger, fear, etc.). Put yourself back into that situation as if it were happening here and now. Recall the details involved, how you felt, how your body felt etc. Now think of one person you would most like to tell about your emotions but have been unable to. Imagine them there with you - visualise them clearly in every detail. Then imagine talking to this person and being able to freely and openly express whatever it is that you felt. Try to get the feeling you are actually talking directly to this person. Examine how you feel in telling them. How do you see them reacting - is it how you thought they would, or different? Now, however you have seen them reacting, change that to the opposite. Examine the differences you feel in yourself and their changes. Compare the two. Then see yourself telling them with their reacting simply with love, forgiveness, understanding, sympathy - whatever you would most care for in the situation. Hold that image for a while and then release.

Another exercise will help you to learn to love yourself.

Close your eyes and be still. Listen to your breathing. Release the tensions within you as you breathe normally and comfortably. Just let them go on the outgoing breath. Go on to explore your skin. Feel your fingers, the touch of your hand against another part of your body. Become aware of the texture of the floor, chair, your clothing, hair, skin, etc. As you explore yourself and your surroundings, listen to what your body tells you and what images come to mind as you experience the touch and connectedness with all around and within you. Then silently repeat to yourself the following:

"I am in touch with my feelings and being. I love myself for I am a member of the universe. A part of the whole. This is a precious possession. I can love myself. I feel safe, secure and at home within my own body. My body is a safe and pleasurable place to be. Whenever I become anxious or afraid or feel that I am unloved I can relax, breathe and feel safe in my body again. I love myself no matter what. I deserve to be loved, and am loved, and therefore can extend my overwhelming sense of love out to all."

As you learn to love yourself, you can encourage that loving energy to flow by giving out love. Put love into the things you do during the day. Give out love to a plant or an animal, or to someone that you don't want it back from. Give it out in the form of a smile, or a compliment and remember that as you give a positive stroke to someone else, they are likely to give you one in return. A recently reported study described how elderly people who looked after a dog or a cat were found to have a better record of health and fewer ailments than their conterparts without pets.

Clearly this illustrates the point about love. Love is an energy. If you put it out trustingly it will not evaporate, it will come back to you. But remember that if you are weighing up what you are going to get in return, then you are not really giving love at all.

Although I have discussed ways of changing your attitude toward yourself and life, there may be problems in other areas of your life that are affecting your health. Often a patient will be anxious about something but does not know what to do about it or feels frightened of tackling it. This is when worry starts. Worry invariably makes you feel worse and it never solves the problem anyway. So, why worry?

It is important to realize that anxiety itself is not a symptom that there is something wrong with you. It is a signal that something is wrong that you should take some action about. This kind of signal releases hormones that prepare your mind and body for action, and the best way to deal with it is to take action.

There is an old fairy story about a huge monster that lived high in the mountains above a village. It was so gigantic that all the villagers were terrified of it. Occasionally it blew puffs of smoke and flame at them, and when they ran away the monster grew bigger than before.

One day one of the villagers decided to do something about this monster that had been terrifying everyone. He set off up the mountain with a stout stick in search of the monster. Something odd began to happen. The closer he got to the monster, the smaller it became. Until, when he came face to face with it, the monster was only the size of a mouse.

Many of our fears are like that. The more we run away from them, the greater they become. If you reverse the process and actually do something about them, you will be putting your attention and energy into what you are doing and the fear and anxiety will diminish.

I suspect that many problems, especially those which affect relationships, are problems of communication. Many people bottle up their problems because they are ashamed of needing help. Human beings are really group animals. We are not meant to cope alone, and there are always people available who are only too glad to help others. I always feel that the best form of help is when the other person enables you to find your *own* answers, rather than telling you what to do. Certainly this is the way in which I prefer to work.

Talking things out with someone else can be helpful in several ways. For example, bringing an anxiety out into the open takes some of the edge off it. Often someone else who is not so close to your problems can see them in a completely different perspective. Talking to someone who accepts you and understands you will also help you feel like the normal, worthwhile person you really are. The knowledge that there is something you can do will help you to regain your self-worth.

No one can wave a magic wand and change you. But once you start letting go of fears and negative thinking about yourself and the world, and putting something more positive in, the clouds *will* start to roll away and you will start the process of self-healing.

- Rauscher, E.A.: Remote Perception of Target Drawings By

(Content)

M.M.;
- Mullins, H.: Judging the Remote Viewing Experiment;
- Mishlove, J.: ESP Dispacement in Free Response Tests with M.M.;
Part Three - Psychokinesis Experiments
- Jungerman, J.A.: PK Experiments with M.M.;
- Deamer, D.W.: Observations Utilizing Biological Materials;
- Lorenz, F.W.: Experiments with M.M.;
- Hickman, J.L., Dakin, H.S.: Electrical Field and Temperature Measurements;
- Lorenz, F.W.: Electroencephalogram Experiments with M.M.;
- Millay, J.: Comments on Lorenz's EEG Experiment;
- Hickman, J.L.: Plant Growth Experiments with M.M.;
- Jungerman, J.A. and Jungerman R.L.: Micro Psi Tests with M.M.;
- Manning, M.: Epilogue.
8) Gregory, A.: London Experiments with Matthew Manning, Proceedings of the Society for Psychical Research, Vol. 56, part 212, Oct. 1982, p. 284 - 302.
9) Barrington, M.R., Bean Growth Promotion Pilot Experiment, London Experiments with Matthew Manning, Proceedings of the Society for Psychical Research, Vol. 56, part 212, Oct. 1982, p. 302 - 304.
10) Ellison, A.J.: Pendulum Experiment, London Experiments, Proceedings SPR, Vol. 56, 1982, p. 304 - 305.
11) Ellison, A.J.: Random Event Generator Experiment, London Experiments, Proceedings SPR, Vol. 56, 1982, p. 305 - 307.
12) Gregory, A.: Poetry Experiments, London Experiments, Proceedings SPR, Vol. 56, 1982, p. 307 - 311.
13) Gregory, A., Wilson, K.: Infra-red Experiments, London Experiments, Proceedings SPR, Vol. 56, 1982, p. 311 - 348.
14) Hasted, J.B.: Experiments on possible psychic effects on the growth rate of moulds, London Experiments, Proceedings SPR, Vol. 56, 1982, p. 349 - 352.
15) Manning, M.: The Subject's Report, London Experiments, Proceedings SPR, Vol. 56, 1982, p. 353 - 361.
16) Inglis, B.: Comments, London Experiments, Proceedings SPR, Vol. 56, 1982, p. 361 - 362.

17) Gregory, A.: Postscript, London Experiments, Proceedings SPR, Vol. 56, 1982, p. 363 - 366.
18) Vernon Harrison: The Signatures on the Walls of Queen's House, Linton, Cambridgeshire and some of the Automatic Scripts and Drawings of Matthew Manning: An Appraisal. Proceedings of the Society for Psychical Research, Vol. 58, Part 218, October 1994.
19) Rein, G.: A psychokinetic effect on the activity of the enzime Monoamine oxidase, private report, 1982.

Recommended reading:

Dolores Krieger: The Therapeutic Touch, Prentice Hall;

Betty Edwards: Drawing on the right side of the brain, Fontana;

Barbra Vitalis: Unicorns are real, Jalmar Press, California;

Gerry Jampolski: Love is letting go of fear, Bantam Books;

Bernie S. Siegel: Love, Medicine & Miracles, 1986, S. Korman & A. Schiff for Bernard S. Siegel, M.D., Children's Trust.

Ram Dass: Be Here Now;

Norman Cousins: The Anatomy of an Illness, Bantam Books;

Michael Talbot: The Holographic Universe, Harper Perennial;

Matthew Manning: The Link, The Extraordinary Gifts of a Teenage Psychic, Colin Smythe Ltd., ISBN 0-86140-283-9, 1974; (The Link has been translated into 16 different languages and more than 1 million copies are sold. The Link is still in print.)

Matthew Manning: In the Mind of Millions, 1977, W.H. Allen Ltd.;

Matthew Manning: The Strangers, 1978, W. H. Allen Ltd., (re-published in 1995 by Colin Smythe Ltd., ISBN 0-86140-381-8);

Matthew Manning: Matthew Manning's Guide to Self-Healing, A positive plan for getting better and staying well, Thorsons Publishers Ltd., 1989. (The book is published in 5 different languages.)

Recommended listening:

Instrumental music for relaxation and healing.

Kitaro: Mandala
Kitaro: Ki
Kitaro: Oasis
Kitaro: Silk Road
Kitaro: Tun Huang
Kitaro: Heaven and Earth
Kitaro: The Best of Kitaro
Vangelis: 1492
Vangelis: China
Vangelis: Antarctica
Vangelis: Soil Festivities
Vangelis: Chariots of Fire
Sacred Spirit: Sacred Spirit
Mike Rowland: Fairy Ring
Mike Rowland: Silver Wings
Mike Rowland: And so to Dream
Tim Wheater: Calmer Panorama
Tim Wheater: Whalesong
Tim Wheater: Eclipse
Tim Wheater: Fish Nite Moon
Nigel Shaw: Seventh Wave
The Enid: The Seed and the Sower

Recordings by Matthew Manning:
(available on cassettes)

Just Relax
Creative Visualisation
Fighting Back
Lifting Depression
The Miracle of Love
Cancer: A positive approach for women
Cancer: A positive approach for men
Controlling Weight Problems
Improving Defective Eyesight
Release from Pain
Release from Phobias
The Healing Touch

Addresses of suppliers:

Matthew Manning's recordings supplied in Great Britain by:
Arnica House
Dept MM Tapes
170 Campden Hill Road
London W8 7AS
Telephone 938 3788.

Matthew Manning's recordings supplied in Europe by:
Eikstein Publications
N-4532 Øyslebø
Norway
Telephone int + 47 382 87780.

How to contact Matthew Manning:

Private consultations:
Matthew Manning
B. O. Box 100
Bury St. Edmunds
Suffolk IP29 4DE, Great Britain
Telephone 01284 830 222, Fax 01284 830 228.

Workshops and healing circles in Great Britain and countries outside Europe:
New Life Promotions
170 Campden Road
London W8 7AS
Telephone 0171 938 3788.

Workshops and healing circles in Europe:
Walter Kraus
N-4532 Øyslebø
Norway
Telephone int + 47 382 87780.